Cover Artist: **Fico Ossio**
Series Edits: **David Hedgecock**
Collection Edits: **Justin Eisinger & Alonzo Simon**
Collection Designer: **Tom B. Long**
Bio designs by: **Sam Barlin**

For internationa
please contact **licensing @idwpublishi**

HC ISBN: 978-1-63140-520-4   TPB ISBN: 978-1-63140-588-4   19 18 17 16   1 2 3

IDW
www.IDWPUBLISHING.com

ACTIVISION.®

Facebook: **facebook.com/idwpublishing**
Twitter: **@idwpublishing**
YouTube: **youtube.com/idwpublishing**
Tumblr: **tumblr.idwpublishing.com**
Instagram: **instagram.com/idwpublishing**

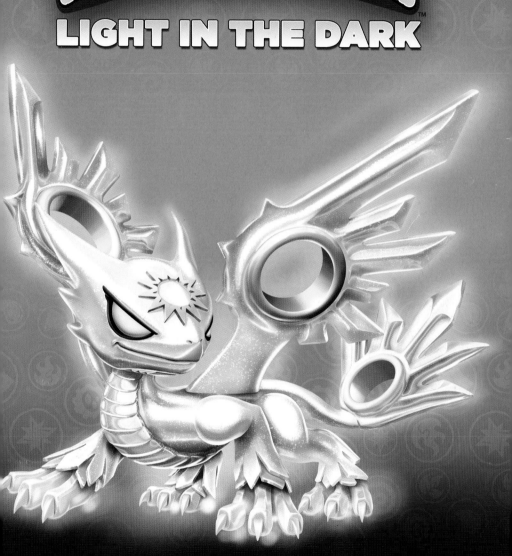

LIGHT SHOW!

Written by: **RON MARZ** & **DAVID A. RODRIGUEZ**
Art by: **FICO OSSIO**
Colors by: **DAVID GARCIA CRUZ**
Letters by: **DERON BENNETT**
Edits by: **DAVID HEDGECOCK**

EN

The FAST and The SPURIOUS!

ten by: **RON MARZ & DAVID A. RODRIGUEZ**
Art by: **DAVID BALDEÓN**
ors by: **DAVID GARCIA CRUZ**
ers by: **DERON BENNETT**

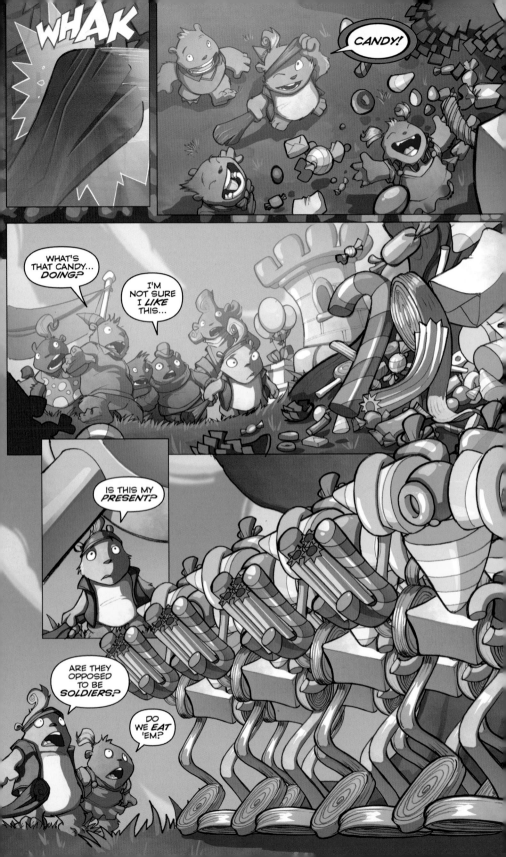

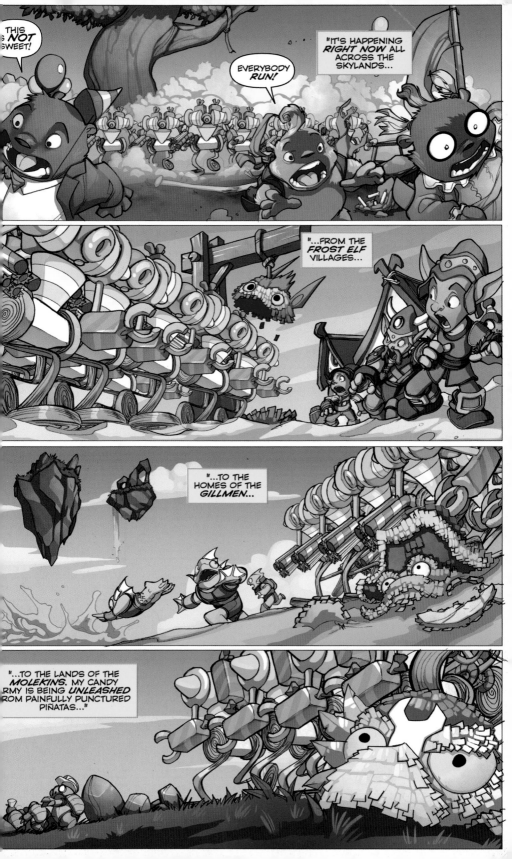

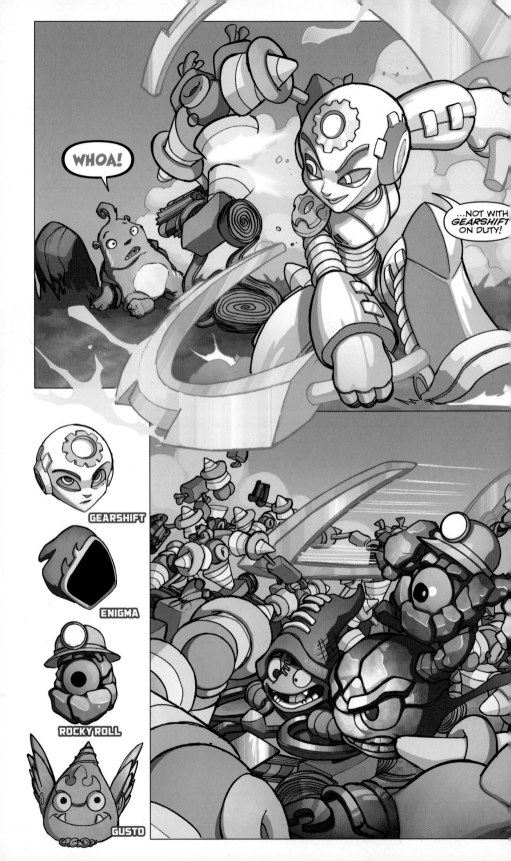

THANKS FOR SAVING US, ROBOT LADY, BUT THERE ARE *MORE* CANDY SOLDIERS ON THE WAY.

DON'T WORRY, I KNOW...

...THAT'S WHY I BROUGHT *FRIENDS*.

OKAY, SKYLANDERS, LET'S GET *ALL GEARED UP!*

LOB-STAR

KABOOM

TUFF LUCK

SHORT CUT

WE'RE *OUTNUMBERED*. OUR BACKS ARE TO THE WALL...

...*LITERALLY*.

BUT WE'RE *NOT* GOING TO B[E] DEFEATED, BECAUS[E] WE'RE *SKYLANDE[RS]*. I NEED YOU TO *FIG[HT]* LIKE YOU'VE NEVE[R] FOUGHT BEFORE. *ALL* OF YOU...

...GUSTO, SHORT CUT...

...KABOOM, TUFF LUCK, ENIGMA...

...LOB-STAR, ROCKY ROLL...

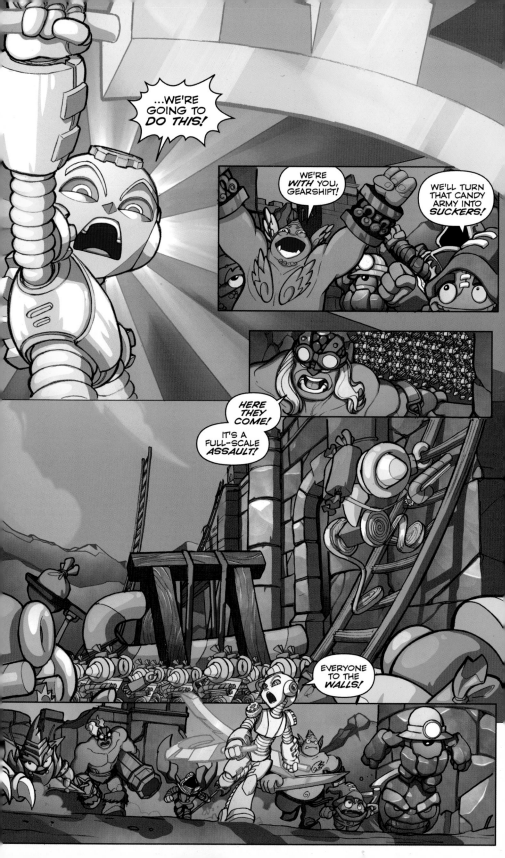

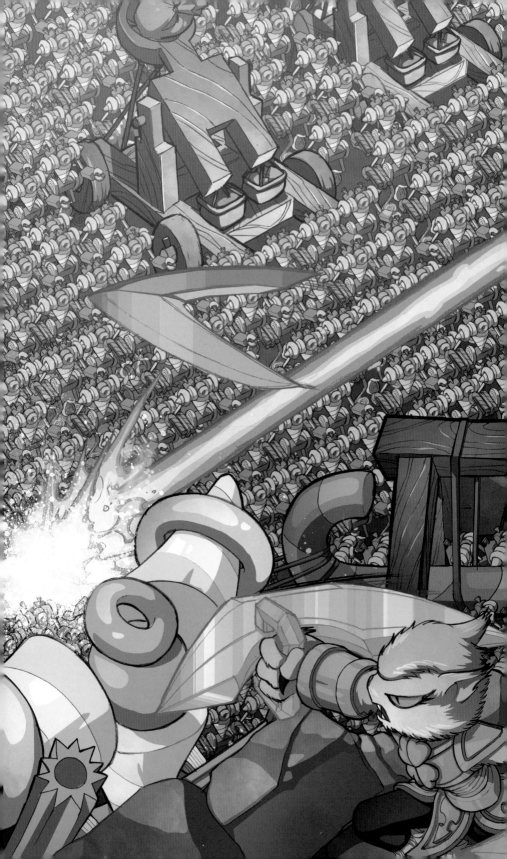

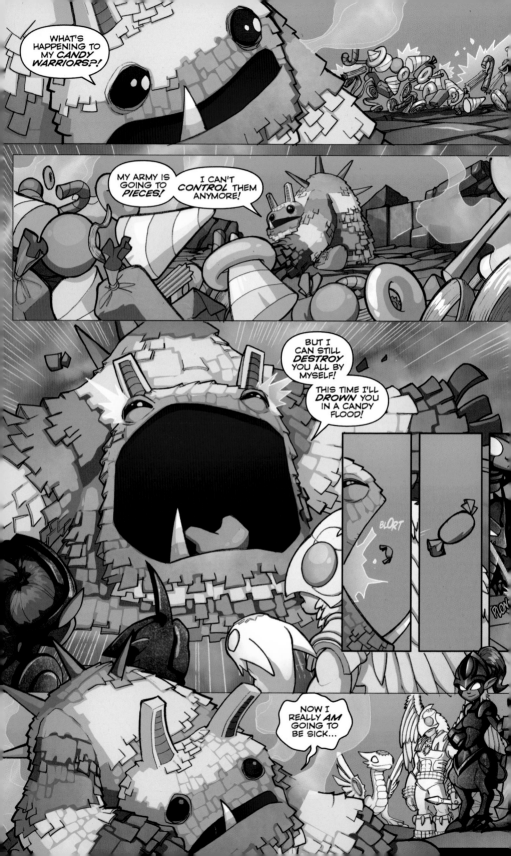

THE ENTIRETY OF THE SKYLANDS OWES *EACH* OF YOU A GREAT DEBT...

...BECAUSE WITHOUT YOUR *COURAGE,* AND YOUR FIERCE FIGHTING SKILLS, PAIN-YATTA MIGHT WELL HAVE CONQUERED ALL OF US!

THAT'S TOO SCARY TO EVEN *THINK ABOUT,* MASTER EON!

I SALUTE THOSE WHO BRAVELY *HELD OUT* AGAINST PAIN-YATTA'S CANDY ARMY...

...AND I ESPECIALLY SALUTE *KNIGH MARE,* SPOTLIG *KNIGHT LIGHT,* A *BLACKOUT.*

YOUR DARK AND LIGHT POWERS BROUGH THE SKYLANDERS THEIR *SWEETEST* VICTORY EVER!

WHAT DO WE *DO?* IF WE KNOCK KAOS INTO THE *MAGICAL LAVA,* HE'LL TAKE GILL RUNT WITH HIM!

DO IT! NOTHING ELSE MATTERS, AS LONG AS WE *DEFEAT* KAOS!

YOU *SKYLOSERS* WOULD *NEVER* SACRIFICE ONE OF YOUR OWN!

NO INTERRUPTION OF *THIS* ERUPTION!

WE HAVE TO *DO* SOMETHING!

WE'RE RUNNING OUT OF *TIME,* PET VAC!

YOU'RE THE *MISSION LEADER!* WHAT'S THE *CALL?!*

I'M NOT...

...I'M NOT SURE WHAT TO *DO!*

THE MISSION IS TO *DEFEAT* KAOS, BUT IS THAT REALLY WORTH *LOSING* GILL RUNT?

TOO LATE!

I'VE ALREADY *WON!*

PAUSE SIMULATION.

YOU HAVE *FAILED* THE TEST, PET VAC. DO YOU KNOW *WHY?*

BECAUSE KAOS *WON.*

THE MISSION WAS TO *DEFEAT* KAOS BUT I COULDN'T *STOP* HIM. I WAS THE TEAM LEADER SO IT'S *MY* FAULT.

THAT IS *NOT* THE REASON. SKYLANDERS ARE NOT EXPECTED TO WIN *EVERY* FIGHT. YOU WILL FAIL AS OFTEN AS YOU *SUCCEED.*

BUT EVEN WHEN FACED WITH AN *IMPOSSIBLE* SITUATION, A LEADER MUST *CHOOSE.* YOU MUST BE ABLE TO MAKE THE *HARD* DECISIONS THAT SEEM IMPOSSIBLE.

THINK ON *THAT,* AND YOU'LL HAVE A CHANCE TO *RETAKE* THE TEST BEFORE GRADUATION.

THIS LIBRARY IS *SO HUGE...*

...BUT I THINK WE'VE FOUND *EVERY* BOOK THAT CAN HELP YOU, PET VAC.

THANKS, HIJINX. THANKS TO *ALL* YOU GUYS...

...BUT I'M NOT SURE *ANYTHING'S* GOING TO HELP ME.

I'LL *NEVER* BE A LEADER, WHICH MEANS I'[LL] NEVER BE A TRU[E] *SKYLANDER.*

YOU HAVE TO *BELIEVE* IN YOURSELF, PET VAC.

EASY FOR *YOU* TO SAY, WEERUPTOR. YOU'RE NOT A *FAILURE.*

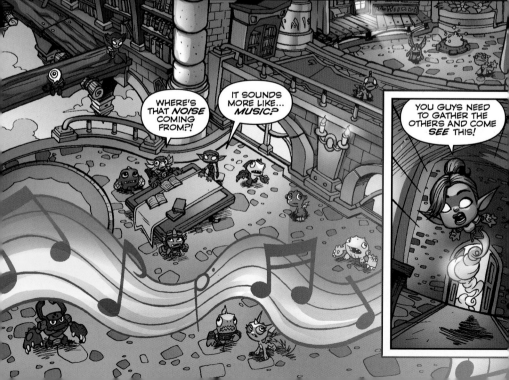

WHERE'S THAT *NOISE* COMING FROM?!

IT SOUNDS MORE LIKE... *MUSIC?*

YOU GUYS NEED TO GATHER THE OTHERS AND COME *SEE* THIS!

NOW THAT'S SOLID GOLD!

WHEN THE *REST* OF THE SKYLANDERS RETURN, THEY'LL MEET THE SAME *GOLDEN FATE*...

...AND THAT WILL BE THE *END* OF THE SKYLANDERS FOREVER!

IT'S THE *GOLDEN QUEEN* AND THE *DOOM RAIDERS!* WHAT ARE *THEY* DOING HERE?!

THEIR ATTACK MUST HAVE TAKEN ALL THE GROWN-UPS BY *SURPRISE.* EVERYONE IN THE COURTYARD HAS BEEN TURNED TO GOLD...

...TESSA, POP FIZZ, HUGO, CALI, EVEN FLYNN!

WHAT ARE WE SUPPOSED TO DO? THE DOOM RAIDERS ARE *WAY* TOO POWERFUL FOR US!

MAYBE WE CAN REACH THE PORTAL CHAMBER AND CALL FOR *HELP?*

YOU HAVE TO LEAD US, PET VAC!

I'VE ALREADY FAILED *ONCE* TODAY.

YOU NEED SOMEONE *ELSE* TO LEAD YOU IF WE'RE GOING TO HAVE ANY HOPE OF SAVING EVERYONE.

WE HAVE TO DO THIS *OURSELVES,* AND EON MADE YOU TEAM LEADER FOR A *REASON,* PET VAC.

REMEMBER, EVEN *SKYLANDERS* FAIL ALL THE TIME. THEY'RE NOT GREAT BECAUSE THEY ALWAYS *WIN,* THEY'RE GREAT BECAUSE THEY *NEVER* GIVE UP!

YOU MUST BE ABLE TO MAKE THE HARD DECISIONS THAT SEEM IMPOSSIBLE.

ALL RIGHT, IF WE CAN'T BEAT THEM *ALL,* WE'LL TAKE THEM ON *ONE* AT A TIME!

HERE'S WHAT WE'RE GOING TO DO...

LOOK AT THESE DIPLOMAS!

NOT *ONE* OF THESE SO-CALLED STUDENTS HAS WHAT IT TAKES TO EARN A POST-GRADUATE DEGREE IN *EVIL.* WHAT A WASTE.

HEY, DOCTOR *STUPID FACE!*

HUH?

SWOOSH

LOOKS LIKE HE *WET HIMSELF!*

YOU WRETCHED LITTLE *RUNTS...*

NO, *I'M* GILL RUNT, THAT'S *TERRABITE* AND *THUMPLING...*

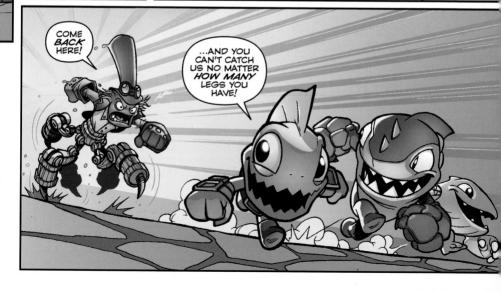

COME *BACK* HERE!

...AND YOU CAN'T CATCH US NO MATTER *HOW MANY* LEGS YOU HAVE!

WE TOTALLY *DID IT!*

PET VAC'S PLAN *WORKED!*

WAIT... WHERE *IS* PET VAC?

HE'S DEFINITELY NOT *HERE*, WHISPER ELF. NOW I'M WORRIED HE'S TRYING TO DO *TOO MUCH* ON HIS OWN...

"...LIKE MAYBE TRYING TO TAKE ON THE GOLDEN QUEEN ALL BY HIMSELF!"

SOMETHING'S NOT RIGHT, BUT I WON'T LET THIS *GOLDEN OPPORTUNITY* SLIP AWAY.

AAH!

FWOOSH

EGGS ARE SO *FRAGILE.* MAYBE *I'D* BETTER HOLD ON TO THIS.

ZZZAP

GIVE THAT *BACK*, YOU FLYING NUISANCE!

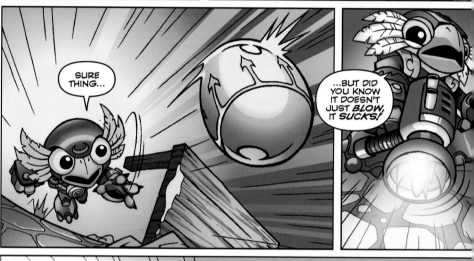

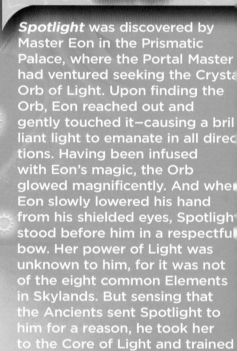

BIO

Spotlight was discovered by Master Eon in the Prismatic Palace, where the Portal Master had ventured seeking the Crysta Orb of Light. Upon finding the Orb, Eon reached out and gently touched it—causing a bril liant light to emanate in all direc tions. Having been infused with Eon's magic, the Orb glowed magnificently. And when Eon slowly lowered his hand from his shielded eyes, Spotligh stood before him in a respectful bow. Her power of Light was unknown to him, for it was not of the eight common Elements in Skylands. But sensing that the Ancients sent Spotlight to him for a reason, he took her to the Core of Light and trained her to defend it as a member of the Skylanders. And when none other than evil Portal Master KAOS destroyed it— *Spotlight* vanished!

BLACKOUT

BIO

Blackout hails from the Realm of Dreams, where the collective imagination of all the creatures in the universe comes together to create beautiful wonders... and terrible nightmares. At a young age, he was recruited into the Dark Stygian—a Dragon Clan whose chief responsibility was to create nightmares for evil creatures as a way to discourage them from doing more villainy. But the clan began to abuse its power and soon spread nightmares far and wide for its own amusement. But Blackout would not stand for it. So he learned to teleport directly into the nightmares the clan created and fought the creatures within. Eventually, the nightmares reached as far as Master Eon, who witnessed Blackout's courage within his own dreams. After helping him put a stop to the Dark Stygian, Eon then made Blackout a Skylander, serving as the protector of the Realm of Dreams and beyond!

KNIGHT MARE

BIO

Before the destruction of the Core of Light left her stranded in the Dark Realm, *Knight Mare* was one of the Dark Centaurs who guarded The Oracle of Stones—an enchanted game of Dark Skystones that could predict the future. When it was stolen by an unknown force, Knight Mare was called upon to retrieve it. She knew it would be dangerous because if the Oracle was asked the wrong questions seven times, it would unleash a terrible curse upon all of Skylands. Fortunately, she found it in a cave—with a gang of Bicyclopes about to ask their seventh wrong question. With no time to lose, she charged forward, beating the fierce Bicyclopes and saving Skylands from the terrible curse. Now having joined the Trap Team, Knight Mare uses her hunting skills and Traptanium Lance to bring down evil everywhere!

KNIGHT LIGHT

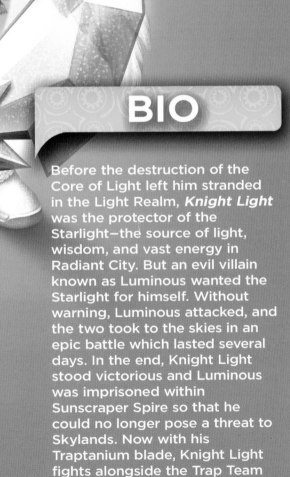

BIO

Before the destruction of the Core of Light left him stranded in the Light Realm, *Knight Light* was the protector of the Starlight—the source of light, wisdom, and vast energy in Radiant City. But an evil villain known as Luminous wanted the Starlight for himself. Without warning, Luminous attacked, and the two took to the skies in an epic battle which lasted several days. In the end, Knight Light stood victorious and Luminous was imprisoned within Sunscraper Spire so that he could no longer pose a threat to Skylands. Now with his Traptanium blade, Knight Light fights alongside the Trap Team to keep evil at bay!

SKYLANDERS™ THE KAOS TRAP
ISBN: 978-1-63140-141-1

SKYLANDERS™ CHAMPIONS
ISBN: 978-1-63140-229-6

SKYLANDERS™ RETURN OF THE DRAGON KING
ISBN: 978-1-63140-268-5

IDW

WWW.IDWPUBLISHIN

© 2016 Activision Publishing, Inc.
and ACTIVISION are registered tr
Activision Publishing, Inc.